THE
Plumber

Peter Leigh

Published in association with
The Basic Skills Agency

Hodder & Stoughton
A MEMBER OF THE HODDER HEADLINE GROUP

Acknowledgements
Cover: Darren Lock
Illustrations: Josephine Blake

Orders: please contact Bookpoint Ltd, 130 Milton Park, Abingdon, Oxon OX14 4SB.
Telephone: (44) 01235 827720, Fax: (44) 01235 400454. Lines are open from 9.00 -
6.00, Monday to Saturday, with a 24 hour message answering service. Email
address: orders@bookpoint.co.uk

British Library Cataloguing in Publication Data
A catalogue record for this book is available from The British Library

ISBN 0 340 84899 5

First published 2002
Impression number   10 9 8 7 6 5 4 3 2 1
Year   2007 2006 2005 2004 2003 2002

Typeset by SX Composing DTP, Rayleigh, Essex.
Printed in Great Britain for Hodder & Stoughton Educational, a division of Hodder
Headline Plc, 338 Euston Road, London NW1 3BH by Athenaeum Press,
Gateshead, Tyne & Wear.

About the Play

The People
- **Mr Smith**
- **Jack**

The Place
The office of Smith's Plumbing.

What's happening
Mr Smith *is sat at his desk. He is talking on the phone and looking at a letter.*

Mr Smith	Listen, Anne.
	As soon as Jack comes in,
	I want to see him.
	Is that clear, Anne?
	As soon as he comes in . . .
	Oh, he's there now, is he?
	Send him right in, then.

He puts the phone down.
The door opens and **Jack** *comes in.*
He has big bandages on his thumb,
on his foot, and round his head.

Mr Smith	Ah, Jack. Good morning.
	I'm glad you could make it.
	Do come in and sit down.

Jack *hobbles in slowly*
and sits very carefully.

	Right, is that OK?
Jack	Yes sir.
Mr Smith	Are you sure?
	Do you want another cushion?

1

Jack	No, sir. I'm fine.
Mr Smith	Good, Jack. Good.
	As long as you're comfortable.
Jack	I am, sir. I am.
Mr Smith	Good.
	Now, Jack. I've got your letter here.
Jack	Yes, sir.
Mr Smith	It's a very interesting letter, Jack.
	It's why I've asked you
	to come in here.
Jack	Yes, sir.
Mr Smith	Now Jack, you say in this letter
	that you want sick leave.
Jack	Yes, sir.
Mr Smith	You want sick leave
	because of a black eye?
Jack	Yes, sir. I can hardly see out of it.
Mr Smith	And because of a swollen toe?
Jack	Yes, sir. I can't walk.
Mr Smith	And because of a sore thumb?
Jack	I can't hold anything
	with that hand, sir.

Mr Smith	And because of a bruised bottom?
Jack	I can hardly sit down, sir.
Mr Smith	And last of all,
	because of concussion?
Jack	Yes, sir, I'm still all dizzy.
Mr Smith	And you also say that
	you want compensation?
Jack	That's right, sir.
	I got these injuries
	while I was working for you.
	So I want compensation.
Mr Smith	And you also want travel expenses
	for four trips to the hospital?
Jack	That's right, sir.
Mr Smith	That's quite a list, Jack.
Jack	It is, sir.
Mr Smith	It adds up to quite a lot, Jack.
Jack	It does, sir.
Mr Smith	Especially since you've only been
	working here for one day, Jack.
Jack	Yes, sir. I started
	yesterday morning.

Mr Smith	And you only had three jobs yesterday . . .
Jack	Yes, sir.
Mr Smith	. . . at Mrs Brown's . . .
Jack	Yes, sir.
Mr Smith	. . . at Mr Jones's . . .
Jack	Yes, sir.
Mr Smith	. . . and at the laundry.
Jack	Yes, sir. That's right, sir.
Mr Smith	Well Jack, now how can I put this? It's not that we don't believe you, Jack, but we do need a little bit more.
Jack	More?
Mr Smith	Yes, Jack. More explanation. You see, Jack, I have a duty to the firm.
Jack	Of course, sir.
Mr Smith	I do have to check all claims. And before I can pass this claim, I do need more explanation.
Jack	Of course, sir.

Mr Smith	You see, take this first one – Mrs Brown.
Jack	Where I got the black eye.
Mr Smith	Yes. But Jack, it was only a blocked tap, that's all.
Jack	Yes sir. That's what you said, sir. 'Mrs Brown has a blocked tap.' But you didn't tell me *what* was blocking Mrs Brown's tap.
Mr Smith	What was blocking Mrs Brown's tap?
Jack	Mrs Brown. Well, not all of her. Just her toe.
Mr Smith	Her toe? And where was the tap?
Jack	In the bathroom.
Mr Smith	Ah, I see. The tap was in the bathroom . . .
Jack	Yes, sir.
Mr Smith	. . . and Mrs Brown's toe was in the tap . . .
Jack	Yes, sir.
Mr Smith	. . . and Mrs Brown was . . .

Jack	. . . in the bath. Yes, sir.
Mr Smith	And how did Mrs Brown's toe get in the tap?
Jack	I didn't ask, sir. None of my business.
Mr Smith	Quite right, Jack. And I don't suppose Mrs Brown was wearing any . . .
Jack	Oh yes, she was, sir. She was all wrapped up in a towel. Not that I looked. I kept my eyes right on the job.

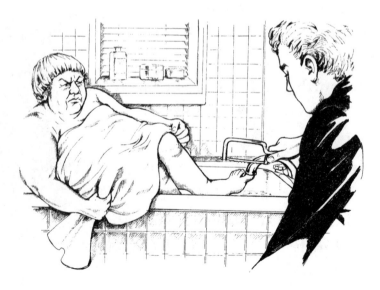

Mr Smith	Good for you.
	And did you get her toe
	out of the tap?
Jack	Yes, but I had to saw it off.
Mr Smith	You had to saw her toe off?
Jack	Not her toe, the tap.
Mr Smith	Oh, so that was all right.
Jack	Well, not exactly.
Mr Smith	What do you mean – not exactly?
	What happened then?
Jack	Well, I sawed the tap off,
	and got her toe out.
	But by this time there was
	a lot of water on the floor.
Mr Smith	Ah, I see.
	You slipped on the water and
	that's how you got the black eye.
Jack	No.
Mr Smith	No?
Jack	No. You see, Mrs Brown started
	to mop the water up with a towel.

Mr Smith	Yes?
Jack	But it was only a little towel.
	So I said, 'You need a bigger towel.'
Mr Smith	Yes?
Jack	But I had forgotten she was
	wearing a towel.
Mr Smith	Yes?
Jack	And she is a large lady.
Mr Smith	Oh, I see . . .
Jack	So when I said,
	'You need a bigger towel . . .'
Mr Smith	. . . she thought you meant her . . .
Jack	Yes! She's got a good
	left hook, Mrs Brown has.
	It came to me before I could duck.
Mr Smith	And that's how you got
	your black eye?
Jack	Yes.
Mr Smith	And that was the first trip
	to the hospital?
Jack	Yes.
Mr Smith	And what about the rest?

Jack	Well, when the hospital had finished patching me up, I thought I better go on to Mr Jones.
Mr Smith	Ah yes, that was with Jim, wasn't it? Mr Jones wanted some pipework doing.
Jack	Yes, sir. Jim was waiting for me, and I was already late. Well, when I got there, Jim had already started. He had started lifting the pipes. He was carrying one when I arrived.
Mr Smith	So?
Jack	Well, they're heavy those pipes, and Jim asked me where I'd been. So I told him, and he started laughing. He seemed to think it was funny. Well, he laughed so much, he dropped the pipe.

Mr Smith	And he dropped it – don't tell me – on your . . .
Jack	That's right! On my toe.
Mr Smith	So that was your second trip to the hospital?
Jack	Yes.
Mr Smith	What did they say?
Jack	'Oh, you again. You must like it here.'
Mr Smith	Did they patch you up?
Jack	Yes. They said it was badly swollen, but it would be all right.
Mr Smith	So what did you do then?
Jack	I went back to Mr Jones.
Mr Smith	With a black eye and a swollen toe? I'm surprised you didn't go off sick then.
Jack	I didn't like to. I mean, it was my first day. I didn't want to give a bad impression.

Mr Smith	Very good. What happened then?
Jack	Well, Jim had carried on
	and was nearly finished.
	Except there was a problem.
Mr Smith	What was that?
Jack	One of the pipes had
	a big blockage.
	We had to clean it out.
Mr Smith	So?
Jack	Well, we got a line down the pipe.
	Jim held on to one end of the line
	while I went up to the other end
	and got hold of the
	other end of the line.
Mr Smith	Yes?
Jack	And then we pushed and pulled
	to clear the blockage.
	We couldn't shift it.
	Jim pulled, and then I pulled,
	but nothing happened.

	And then Jim grabbed it
	and pulled with all his strength,
	and the blockage came free.
Mr Smith	So that's good, then.
Jack	Except I was still holding on to
	the other end of the line.
	Jim pulled it so hard that
	I was jerked forward
	and I got my thumb
	stuck in the pipe.
Mr Smith	That must have hurt.
Jack	It did. That's why I've got
	a sore thumb.
Mr Smith	Did you get it out of the pipe?
Jack	No! At least not straight away.
	I pushed and I pulled,
	but I couldn't shift it.
	So Jim came round to help.
	I pulled my thumb,
	and Jim pulled me.

Mr Smith	And that worked?
Jack	Sort of. He's strong that Jim.
	He gave one big pull,
	and my thumb came out.
	Trouble was, I wasn't expecting it,
	and I went flying backwards,
	and landed . . .
Mr Smith	Right on your —
Jack	Exactly!
Mr Smith	So now you had a sore thumb
	and a bruised bottom?
Jack	Yes.
Mr Smith	And you went back to the
	hospital?
Jack	Yes.
Mr Smith	I bet they were surprised
	to see you.
Jack	'He's back,' they said,
	and they all cheered.
	I'm their best customer,
	they said.

Mr Smith	Did they fix you up?
Jack	Yes. 'See you soon,' they said as they sent me out.
Mr Smith	So did you go back to Mr Jones?
Jack	No. I thought it was too dangerous there. So I went on to the next job.
Mr Smith	At the laundry?
Jack	Yes. One of the big tumble-driers was broken.
Mr Smith	What was wrong with it?
Jack	It wouldn't work.
Mr Smith	I see. So what did you do?
Jack	Well, you know with those big tumble-driers, you have to crawl right into them to mend them?
Mr Smith	Yes.

Jack	Well, I crawled right into it.
	Even though I had a black eye,
	a swollen toe, a sore thumb,
	and a bruised bottom.
Mr Smith	Very good. And did you mend it?
Jack	Yes.
Mr Smith	How do you know?
Jack	It started to work.
Mr Smith	Right. You mean, it started to
	turn over and over.
Jack	Yes.
Mr Smith	And you were still . . .
Jack	Yes. Still inside it.
Mr Smith	I see. And that's how you
	got your concussion.
Jack	Yes.
Mr Smith	So you went back to the hospital.
Jack	Yes. They had a party for me.
	They were all there –
	all the doctors and nurses.
	They treated me for concussion,
	and also for cracked ribs.

I didn't need that,
but it was a present, they said –
because I was such
a good customer.

Mr Smith And what did you do then?

Jack I went home. I'd had enough.

Mr Smith Right, you went home,
and then you wrote me
a long letter, which I have here.

	In this letter you say
	you want sick leave while
	all these injuries get better . . .
Jack	Yes, sir.
Mr Smith	. . . and you want compensation
	because all these are accidents
	at work.
	So the firm is to blame.
Jack	Yes, sir.
Mr Smith	Right, let's leave that
	just for the moment, Jack,
	because your letter isn't the
	only one I've had this morning . . .

Break.

Mr Smith	. . . In fact, I've got quite a pile.
	The first one is from Mrs Brown.
	In fact it's not a letter, it's a bill.
	It's a bill for one bath tap,
	because you sawed it off.
Jack	Well, it was either that
	or her toe.

Mr Smith	She doesn't think so.
	She thinks you didn't need
	to saw the tap off,
	and if you did,
	you should have replaced it.
Jack	I was going to, but she hit me.
Mr Smith	She says either we pay for the tap
	or she's going to complain
	about us to the papers.
	For rudeness.
Jack	Well, it wasn't my fault.
	It could have happened to
	anyone.
Mr Smith	And then there's a second letter,
	from Mr Jones.
	He seems to think
	that you and Jim laid his pipes
	the wrong way round.
Jack	No, we didn't.
Mr Smith	Well, shall I tell you what he gets
	when he turns his hot tap?
Jack	What?

Mr Smith	Radio One! That's what he gets.
Jack	Well, that's Jim's fault.
	Not mine.
Mr Smith	But you were meant to be
	helping him,
	so there wouldn't be any mistakes.
Jack	But I was injured.
	I had to go to the hospital.
Mr Smith	(*angrily*) Because your thumb
	got stuck in a pipe?
Jack	It wasn't my fault, I tell you.
Mr Smith	And you sat down hard
	on your backside?
	I would have kicked it
	if I'd have been there.
Jack	It was an accident.
	It could have happened to anyone.
Mr Smith	(*calming himself*)
	All right, Jack! All right.
	But now let's look at
	this last letter.

	This is from the laundry.
	You know that drier you mended?
Jack	Yes.
Mr Smith	Well, those driers are
	quite delicate.
	They are meant for clothes –
	clothes, Jack, not heavy plumbers
	and their tools.
	In fact heavy plumbers
	and their tools
	can do quite a lot of damage.
	In fact that's exactly what they did,
	and here's the bill for a new one.
Jack	It was an accident, I tell you.
Mr Smith	Jack, let me tell you
	there is only one accident here.
	Do you know what
	that accident is, Jack? . . .
	It is you, Jack.
Jack	Me?
Mr Smith	Yes, you, Jack!

	You are the biggest accident
	of them all.
	I've never heard
	such nonsense in my life!
Jack	What?
Mr Smith	And then you come in here
	expecting me to believe it all?
	'Dropped the pipe on my foot
	because he was laughing' . . .
	'The tumble-drier started
	while I was inside it'?
Jack	It could happen to anyone.
Mr Smith	Anyone with a brain
	the size of a pea.
Jack	They're accidents, I tell you.
	They could happen to anyone.
	You owe me compensation.
Mr Smith	Oh yes, oh yes. The compensation.
	I'm glad you mentioned that.

	Not only have I got three bills here –
	and not only do you want sick leave
	and travel expenses,
	but on top of all that
	you want me to give you
	compensation.
Jack	It's my right.
Mr Smith	Your right! Your right!
	I know what your right is.
	And I'm going to give it to you.
	Do you know what your right is?
Jack	What?
Mr Smith	The sack, Jack.
	That's what your right is,
	and that's what I'm giving you
	right now.
	Jack, you are fired!
Jack	What? You can't do that!
Mr Smith	Oh, I can't, can't I?
	You see if I can't.
	I want you out of here now.

	Before you do me any more damage.
Jack	I'll get the law on to you. I'll take you to court and take you for every penny you've got.
Mr Smith	Oh yes? Oh yes? Do you think they'll believe you? Are you going to have Mrs Brown wrapped up in a towel as a witness? Or are you going to take the jury down to the laundry to see if they can fit in the tumble-drier?
Jack	They were accidents. They could happen to anyone.
Mr Smith	(*now really angry*) Rubbish! Get out of my office . . . NOW!

Mr Smith *bangs his hand down on the table as he says this, and hits his thumb.*

| | OW!! Now see what you've made me do.
Get out NOW! |
| **Jack** | All right! I'm going, but you haven't heard the last of this. |

Jack *gets up and goes out angrily.*
Mr Smith *sinks into his seat,
nursing his thumb.*

| **Mr Smith** | Oh my poor thumb!
I'd better go to the hospital. |

Mr Smith *picks up the phone,
but he can't hold it properly
because of his thumb.
He drops the phone on to his toe.*

OW! My toe!

*He reaches down to hold his toe,
and picks up the phone.
When he straightens up again
he bangs his head on the desk.*

OW! My head! I'm all dizzy.
I must have concussion.

Finally, he manages to find
the phone and tap a key.

Hello, Anne. Listen.
I'm going to the hospital.
I've got a sore thumb, a sore toe,
and concussion.
It was an accident.
It could happen to anyone.

He puts the phone down,
and sits holding his sore thumb,
his sore toe, and his head.
He is thinking.
Finally he picks up the phone again.

Oh, one other thing, Anne.
Tell Jack he can have
his job back.